This book belongs to

· ·

· ·

Written by Kelly Hargrave

Designed by Deena Fleming

Cover design by Flora Chan

tangerine press

an imprint of
SCHOLASTIC
www.scholastic.com

Copyright © 2017 Scholastic Inc.

Scholastic, Tangerine Press, and associated logos are trademarks and/or registered trademarks of Scholastic Inc.

Published by Tangerine Press, an imprint of Scholastic Inc.,
557 Broadway, New York, NY 10012

10 9 8 7 6 5 4 3 2 1
ISBN: 978-1-338-16614-9

Printed and bound in Jiaxing, China

Kittens are FUR-REAL the meowst adorable creatures on the planet! Get ready for a page-turning cat attack of cuteness. Every day can be Caturday with this pawesome book full of games and activities. Do your thing with colorful pens and pencils, and then check for answers in the back of the book!

Ice Cream Maze

Help Kitty find her way through the ice cream maze to the world's largest ice cream cone!

What's your favorite ice cream flavor?

START HERE

FINISH HERE

Kittens Rule!

...ss Kitty is ready to rule the day! Can you ...her pick out what she should wear to the ball tonight? Circle your choice.

OR

OR

OR

OR

Unicat Magic

You've spotted a rare unicat! Unscramble the colored letters to form the word that matches the image on the right. Then you will discover what kind of magical powers a unicat has.

1. Turns regular milk into *erwsbtryrzt* milk

2. Makes a grilled cheese *kptaser*

3. Leaves *birpawn* paw prints wherever it goes

4. Makes a hedgehog smell like *nmcnanoi* rolls

Answers on page 92

Flower-Crown Doodle

Draw purrty flower crowns on each of the kittens (or use the floral stickers provided in the back of this book).

Fairy Garden

Help Fairy Kitten find all of the flower blossoms shaped like kitten faces.

Answer on page 90.

Merkitten Race

START

START

Watch out for those kitty jellyfish!

START

8

These playful merkittens are about to race!
At the start of each merkitten, follow the maze
to see which one wins!

END

Answer on
page 90.

Kitten Carnival

Each kitten carnival ride has a sign. Use the code to figure out the name of each ride. For rides that have blank signs, come up with your own silly or adorable ride name!

A B C D E F G H I

J K L M N O P Q R

S T U V W X Y Z

3

11

Answers on page 90.

Kitten in a Costume

Can you match the cute, costumed kitty to its shadow? Draw a line from the kitty to the correct shadow.

If you could dress a kitten in any costume, what would it be? Draw or paste your answer here:

13

Answer on page 91.

Spot the Difference

Circle the kitten cupcake that looks different than the others.

Circle the waffle kitten that looks different than the others.

Answers on page 91.

Kitty Superhero Generator

Mix and match words from each column to create exciting superhero kitten names. Try using some of your own words too! Get ready to giggle, because some of these kittens have extremely silly superhero names, like Turbo Invisible Banana Cat!

Fluffy	Fire Breathing	Banana	Kitty
Smelly	Invisible	Taco	Cat
Slimy	Immortal	Pizza	Feline
Curious	Poisonous	Pancake	Creature
Strong	Time-Traveling	Rainbow	Monster
Turbo	Flying	Wizard	Furball
Awesome	High-Fiving	Flower	Hunter
Silly	Battling	Laser	Thief
Cool	Cloning	Dinosaur	Snuggler
Mighty	Magical	Ninja	Dude
Spicy	Shape-Shifting	Galaxy	Whiskers
Adorable	Clawing	Alien	Warrior

_____

_____

_____

_____

_____

_____

_____

Unicat Magic

You've spotted a rare unicat! Unscramble the colored letters to form the word that matches the image on the right. Then you will discover what kind of magical powers a unicat has.

1. Turns regular milk into **erwsbryrat** milk

2. Makes a grilled cheese **kplaser**

3. Leaves **biroawn** paw prints wherever it goes

4. Makes a hedgehog smell like **nmcnanoi** rolls

Answers on page 92.

Pirate Kitty Treasure

Pirate Kitty is on a quest to find shiny, magical kitty treasure! Using the clues, can you figure out which treasure chest is full of Pirate Kitty's favorite treasure?

CLUE 1
Pirate Kitty's treasure has a shiny blue milk bottle.

CLUE 2
Her treasure chest doesn't have a heart-shaped lock.

CLUE 3
Her treasure has gold coins with cat faces on them.

CLUE 4
Pirate Kitty's treasure has a golden mouse in it.

CLUE 5
Her treasure has a jewel-encrusted food bowl.

Answer on page 92.

Cat Pun Word Search

Can you find all the goofy cat puns in the word search?

Word Key

Purrito

Catton Candy

I Love Meowsic

Cattitude

Catstronaut

Clawesome

Caturday

Avocato

Vampurr

Pawpular

Answer on page 92.

```
Q F A L P S T I U S D N W C G
H C D X R A F Q X M G D Q E C
K X E A A A Q R B P D V U M U
C A T S T R O N A U T B U L D
D G P A W P U L A R R C W F S
C V J N I C Z E X R N P K L I
A K M L Y T L V E I G O P O A
T H Y D N A C N O T T A C N Z
U Q N R R Z P G T O S P Y K R
R R K Y W I Y G N K T L I U R
D N W L H O T A C O V A P T O
A R W V A M P U R R J B Z S S
Y C A T T I T U D E X B S V H
Q U D C L A W E S O M E X C S
D I L O V E M E O W S I C I C
```

La Petite Kitten Kitchen

Chef Kitty is excited to open her own restaurant. From the list below, choose which items should go on each of the menus: breakfast, lunch, dinner, and dessert. Once you've added an item to a menu, cross it off the list so you know you've already used it.

- Catermelon Milkshake
- Spaghetti with Fish Meatballs
- Tuna Ice Cream with Sprinkles
- Fruity Cereal with Kitten Marshmallows
- Creamy Dreamy Milk Soup
- Mashed Potatoes with Mouse Gravy
- Sparkling Sushi Sandwich
- Cat-Eared Doughnut

Answer on page 93.

24

BREAKFAST MENU

....

....

....

LUNCH MENU

....

....

....

DINNER MENU

....

....

....

DESSERT MENU

....

....

....

Try coming up with one or two of your own purr-a-licious menu items!

25

Starry Night

Follow the dotted lines that connect the stars to make twinkly kitty constellations.

It's a Party!

Kitty wants to throw a truly cat-tastic birthday party. Can you help her find each item in the box below in the photo on page 29?

What activities should Kitty do at her birthday party? List them here.

....
....
....
....

Answers on page 93.

Baby Animal BFFs

Circle the cute kitten pairing that reminds you of you and your BFF. Then write about why.

If you and your best friend could have one full day with these cuties, what would you do? Where would you go?

....
....
....
....
....
....

....
....
....

. . . .

. . . .

. . . .

. . . .

. . . .

. . . .

. . . .

. . . .

Space Adventure

Fill in the blanks throughout the story to help Astronaut Kitty make her way through outer space!

Astronaut Kitty took a ride in a spaceship to a planet that no kitty had ever been to before. When she arrived, she was _____ to see weird kitty aliens everywhere! Some of them had _____ heads, three tails, and four _____! There were polka-dotted alien kitties, _____ alien kitties, and even kitties with feathers!

Astronaut Kitty was scared. She was about to fly back to Earth when she noticed one of the aliens was smiling and _____ at her. Then another alien did the same thing, and another, and another.

Feeling brave, Astronaut Kitty stepped out of her spaceship. She was relieved when each alien kitty greeted her with a _____. The alien kitties decided to throw a party for their new guest, with plenty of moon pies, star fruit, and _____!

Design Your Own

Turn these cats into alien kittens. Add antennas, multiple eyes, polka dots, multiple ears, or even two tails. Go alien-kitty crazy!

Ice Cream Maze

Help Kitty find her way through the ice cream maze to the world's largest ice cream cone!

What's your favorite ice cream flavor?

START HERE

FINISH
HERE

37

Answer on
page 93.

Make a Wish ...

You found a pretty, sparkly bottle, and the genie inside is a cute kitten! Genie Kitten can grant you three wishes. If you could wish for [any]thing, what would it be? Write, draw, or paste pictures of your wishes in the clouds.

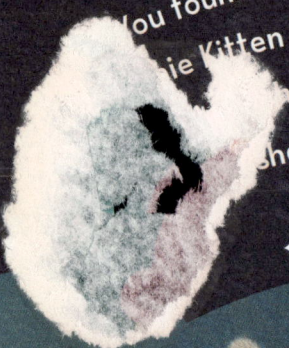

Rainbow Kittens

If each rainbow kitten could smell like something delicious, what would each one smell like? Maybe a yellow kitten smells like a banana split, or a white kitten smells like vanilla frosting. Write your answers next to each colorful kitten!

At the end of every rainbow, there is a pot of gold.

Pardon Me, I'm on the Phone

Match each trendy cat with its exact match.

43

Answer on page 94.

Doodle Your Own Mustache Cats

Draw a pair of glasses and a mustache or a beard on each cat, or use the mustache and glasses stickers provided in the back of the book to decorate.

How to Draw a Kitten

On a separate sheet, follow the steps to draw your very own kitten.

1 Start by drawing two triangles. Then draw a line across the middle to connect the two triangles.

2 Next add a curved line from one triangle ear to the other, as shown below.

3 Now draw in some almond-shaped eyes and a round nose in the middle.

4 Finally, draw a line down from the nose with two curved lines on either side. Add in the whiskers, and you're all done!

Now it's time to draw the body.

1 Start with the kitty face you've drawn on the previous page.

2 Draw a curved line from the face down and around to create the bottom, and back foot.

3 Continue the body by adding in the top foot as shown below.

4 Draw the back two feet by adding in c-shaped feet above the other feet.

5 Next add the tail. You can make it as long or short as you want!

6 Now finish by adding any pattern you want your kitty to have! He can have stripes, spots, or even a rainbow, calico pattern!

Design Diva

Using what you've just learned, cover these T-shirts and phone cases with cute kittens!

Kitten Spa Puzzle

1

Kitty had a purrfect day at the spa with her friends. Can you figure out where the missing puzzle pieces should go to complete the picture?

2

3

Answer on
page 94.

Make Your Own Memes

I'M JUST KITTEN AROUND!

Following the examples, write your own funny lines on each picture to make your own cat memes!

I'M NOT FELINE WELL.

I'M PURRRRTY SICK.

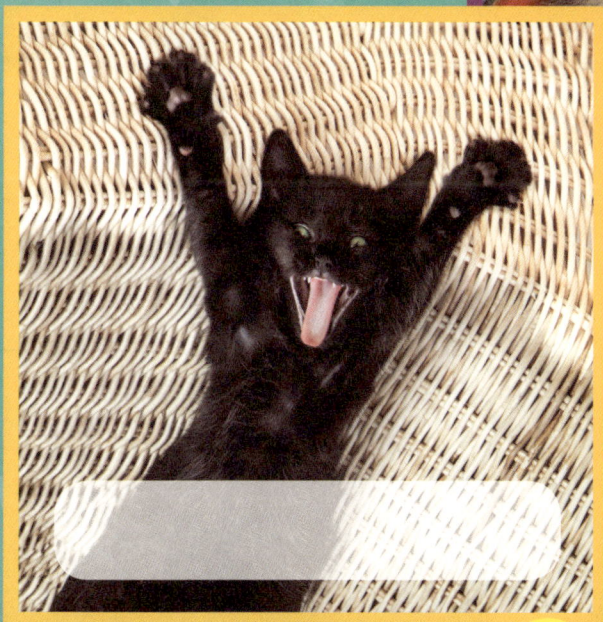

Kittens Rule!

Princess Kitty is ready to rule the day! Can you help her pick out what she should wear to the ball tonight? Circle your choices.

 OR

 OR

 OR

OR

CASTLE
Maze

Princess Kitty is the star of a video game. Help her find a safe path around the two-headed kitty dragon and the creepy kitty ghosts!

START

END

57

Answer on
page 94.

Create Your Own
VIDEO GAME

If you could create your own kitten—inspired video game, what would it be like?
Write it all down here!

Think of things such as:

- What unique or silly characters exist in your video game?
- Are they all kittens, or are there non-kittens too?
- How do the different levels look?
- Is there an exciting new land?
- Do any special items need to be collected? If so, what are they and how do they look?
- Do any of the characters have special powers?
- Are there any villains to defeat? If so, describe them.

Name That Kitten

CALLIE

Write a cute kitten name on each of the kitten tags.

Dreamy Darlings

What is each kitten dreaming about?
Draw their dreams in each of the thought bubbles.

Hollywood Getaway

Help Kitty enjoy her Hollywood getaway by filling in the blanks throughout the story.

Kitty took a hike up to the Hollywood sign to take a few pictures, but when she was done, she was too scared of heights to hike back down. Luckily, she ran into her favorite celebrity, _____! And Kitty was just in luck: her favorite celebrity had a glamorous helicopter pick them up.

Together they explored Hollywood. They went to the beach and built a

_____. They went to a fancy restaurant and ate_____. They even went to the movie set of _____, where they got to meet _____.

At the end of the day, Kitty thanked _____ for hanging out with her. They took a selfie and parted ways. Kitty will never forget her _____ day in Hollywood!

Candy Shop Code

Using the candy code key, match each candy to the letter to figure out what Kitty bought from the candy store!

A	B	C	D	E	F	G	H	I

J	K	L	M	N	O	P	Q	R

S	T	U	V	W	X	Y	Z

Answer on page 95.

Kitten Wedding Cake

These cute kittens are getting married, but they need help picking out the purrfect wedding cake. Using the clues, can you help figure out their purrfect cake? Circle your answer.

CLUE 1
The top layer has white icing.

CLUE 2
All of the layers have flowers.

1

CLUE 3
Both cat figures on top have pink noses.

2

3

CLUE 4
The second layer does not have a heart.

CLUE 5
The plate on the bottom is yellow.

4

Answer on page 95.

Crazy Cat CREATURES

If these kitten-and-animal pairings were combined to make one animal, what would the new kitten creature's name be?
For example, if a dinosaur merged with a cat, it would be a dinocat!
Write the silly name under the pair.

Kitten and an octopus

Kitten and a flamingo

Kitten and a bear

Kitten and a whale

Draw one of your crazy cat creatures here:

Kitten and an alligator

Pawesome Tea Party

Circle the items you think Kitty should have at her tea party!

OR

OR

OR

OR

OR

OR

Kitten

Yoga

Each kitten yoga picture below matches another. Find the pairs!

Answer on page 95.

CATegories Game

Let's play CATegories to see what kind of kitten you will have in the future.

1. How old are you? That is your magic number.
2. Count each item, not the category, and when you get to your magic number, cross that item off.
3. After marking off an item, continue counting and marking off items only when you get to your magic number.
4. When a category has one item left, circle it (you no longer have to include this category in your counting).
5. When each category only has one item left, this is your kitten future!

I will own a:
A) White cat
B) Black cat
C) Orange cat
D) Gray cat

Its name will be:
A) Fluffers McGee
B) Princess Sparkle Paws
C) Repawnzel
D) Catzilla

Its favorite food will be:

A) S'mores
B) Sushi
C) Caramel apples
D) Macaroni and cheese

It will be best friends with a:

A) Koala
B) Penguin
C) Turtle
D) Hedgehog

It will wear:

A) Sunglasses
B) Crown
C) Backpack
D) Cape

It will:

A) Star in a movie
B) Be the first kitten Olympian
C) Blow golden-bubble kisses
D) Have an amusement park named after it

Its hobby will be:

A) Singing songs about kittens
B) Playing video games
C) Tap dancing
D) Painting kitten portraits

Word Play

How many words can you create
using the letters in

KITTEN CUDDLES?

KITTY
Travel Expert

Kitty has taken an adventure to the Big Apple! Can you find Kitty in the photo?

New York

Answer on page 96.

Meow Moods

Match the emoji to the kitten face.

A

B

C

D

1

2

3

4

Answers on page 96.

Kitten Fashion Show

Kitty was invited to be in a fashion show!
Draw outfits on each cat.

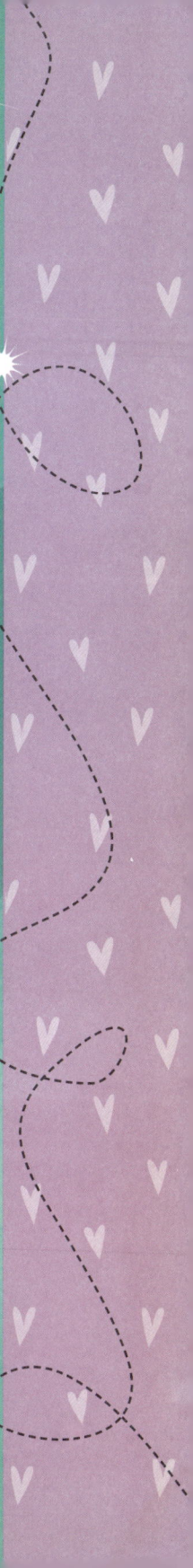

Snowy Day Word Search

It's snowing outside! Complete the snowy word search so Kitty can go outside and play.

Word Key

Mittens

Hat

Coat

Boots

Snowflake

Hot Cocoa

Sled

Snowball

Ice

```
        F S H S I
      J B A P G C B
    G E T T E D E L S
    P M S T O W R U R R
    M U N S A D S S R
    X O N G O M U
    W O O V C
    I F W W F Y A
  K U L B M K C O S
J R U A A I Y I C K G
I F U K L T U I O A G
E C K E L T X U C V H
E V I I P E G I T Y M
B O O T S N Y Y O O S
Y S V B S N Y H B
```

Answer on page 96.

MAGIC SHOW
Scramble

AbraCATabra!

Unscramble the words to discover what items Magician Kitty has pulled out of her hat.

1 tiañap

....

2 msge

....

3 ooshngit tras

....

4 ianrwbo ssreo

....

5 bbelubmug rinhmae

....

6 thlso

....

Answers on page 96.

Answer Key

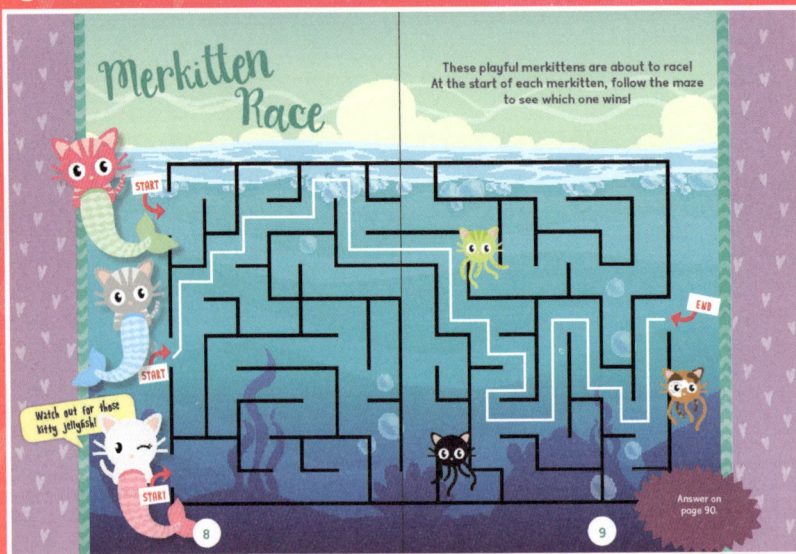

1 Kitty Carousel   **2** Kitten Cups

3 Kooky Kitty Bumper Cars

Page 13

Page 14

Page 15

Page 19

1. strawberry   2. sparkle
3. rainbow   4. cinnamon

Page 21

4

Pages 22–23

```
Q F A L P S T I U S D N W C G
H C D X R A F Q X M G D Q E C
K X E A A A Q R B P D V U M U
C A T S T R O N A U T B U L D
D G P A W P U L A R R C W F S
C V J N I C Z E X R N P K L I
A K M L Y T L V E I G O P O A
T H Y D N A C N O T T A C N Z
U Q N R R Z P G T O S P Y K R
R R K Y W I Y G N K T L I U R
D N W L H O T A C O V A P T O
A R W V A M P U R R J B Z S S
Y C A T T I T U D E X B S V H
Q U D C L A W E S O M E X C S
D I L O V E M E O W S I C I C
```

Pages 24-25

Breakfast Menu: Cat-eared Doughnut,
    Fruity Cereal with Kitten Marshmallows
Lunch Menu: Sparkling Sushi Sandwich,
    Creamy Dreamy Milk Soup
Dinner Menu: Spaghetti with Fish Meatballs,
    Mashed Potatoes with Mouse Gravy
Dessert Menu: Tuna Ice Cream with Sprinkles,
    Catermelon Milkshake

Pages 28-29

Pages 36-37

Pages 42-43

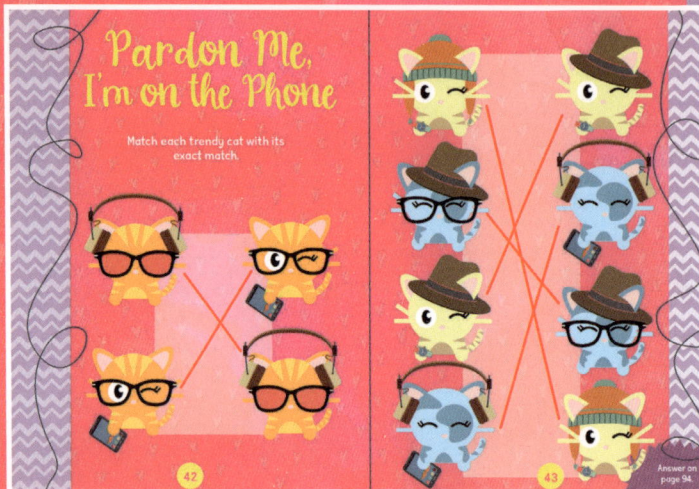

Pardon Me, I'm on the Phone

Match each trendy cat with its exact match.

42

43

Answer on page 94.

Pages 50-51

3

1

2

Page 57

START

END

Pages 66–67

CHOCOLATE CARAMEL LOLLIPOPS AND YUMMY GUMMY MICE

Pages 68–69

3

Pages 74–75

Pages 80–81

Pages 82–83
A: 2   B:1   C: 3   D:4

Pages 86–87

Page 89

1. piñata   2. gems   3. shooting star   4. rainbow roses
5. bubblegum machine   6. sloth